Devon's
Wild & Wicked
WEATHER

Chips Barber

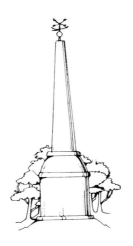

OBELISK PUBLICATIONS

ALSO BY THE AUTHOR:

Ten Family Bike Rides in Devon
Ten Family Walks on Dartmoor • Six Short Pub Walks on Dartmoor
Short Circular Walks in and around Sidmouth • Walks on and around Woodbury Common
Diary of a Dartmoor Walker • Diary of a Devonshire Walker
The Great Little Dartmoor Book • The Great Little Exeter Book
The Great Little Totnes Book • The Great Little Plymouth Book • The Great Little Chagford Book
Made in Devon • The Dartmoor Quiz Book • Place-Names in Devon • An A to Z of Devon Dialect
Dark & Dastardly Dartmoor • The Ghosts of Exeter • Haunted Pubs in Devon
Ghastly & Ghostly Devon • The Lost City of Exeter – Revisited
Exmouth in Colour • Plymouth in Colour • Dawlish and Dawlish Warren in Colour
Beautiful Exeter • Colourful Dartmoor • Colourful Cockington • Topsham in Colour
The South Hams in Colour • Torbay in Colour – Torquay, Paignton, Brixham
Sidmouth Past and Present • Topsham Past and Present • Honiton Past and Present
Seaton & Axmouth • Beer • Branscombe • Colyton & Colyford
Around & About Salcombe • Around & About Teignmouth
Around & About Hope Cove and Thurlestone • Around & About Burgh Island and Bigbury Bay
Around & About Tavistock • Around & About Roborough Down • Around & About Lustleigh
Kingskerswell of Yesteryear *(with John Hand)* • Shaldon & Ringmore
Dawlish and Dawlish Warren • The South Hams • Torquay • Paignton • Brixham
From The Dart to The Start • Dartmouth and Kingswear
Brixham of Yesteryear, Parts I, II and III • Pinhoe of Yesteryear, Parts I and II
Princetown of Yesteryear, Parts I and II • The Teign Valley of Yesteryear, Parts I and II
Widecombe – A Visitor's Guide • Bickleigh – A Visitor's Guide
Newton Ferrers and Noss Mayo • Along The Otter • Along The Tavy • Along The Avon
Railways on and around Dartmoor • Devon's Railways of Yesteryear
Chagford of Yesteryear • Dartmoor of Yesteryear • Exminster of Yesteryear • Dartmouth of Yesteryear
Heavitree of Yesteryear • Sidmouth of Yesteryear • Whipton of Yesteryear
Plymouth Hoe • Tiverton • The Story of Hallsands • The Story of Dartmoor Prison
The Story of Dawlish Warren • Dawlish of Yesteryear • Discovering Devon…Dawlish
Walk the East Devon Coast – Lyme Regis to Lympstone
Walk the South Devon Coast – Dawlish Warren to Dartmouth
Walk the South Hams Coast – Dartmouth to Salcombe
Walk the South Hams Coast – Salcombe to Plymouth

*We have over 200 Devon titles. For a full list of current titles please send SAE to
Obelisk Publications, 2 Church Hill, Pinhoe, Exeter EX4 9ER. Tel: (01392) 468556.*

ACKNOWLEDGEMENTS:

Thanks to Jane Leonard for pictures on pages 11 and 19,
John Bartlett for page 28,
Ben "Silver Fox" King for page 29 (top and middle),
Pat Wills for page 30 (top) and Paul Williams for page 30 (middle and bottom).
All other pictures are by or belong to Chips Barber.

*First published in 2005
by Obelisk Publications, 2 Church Hill, Pinhoe, Exeter, Devon, EX4 9ER
Designed and Typeset by Sally Barber
Printed in Great Britain
by Avocet Press, Cullompton, Devon*

© Chips Barber/Obelisk Publications

Devon's
Wild & Wicked
WEATHER

Introduction

"Looks like rain", "Nice day", or "It's a bit parky!" are the sort of comments we are all familiar with in this country. Whether it's a lack of imagination, or a genuine concern for meteorological conditions, to the rest of the world, the British are obsessed with the weather!

This obsession is understandable in Devon: after all, we are home to the Meteorological Office. We also get 'non-stop' weather, which can change within minutes – ask any seasoned Dartmoor walker. They will tell you that one moment it can be gloriously warm and sunny, but the next minute they need to raid their rucksacks for protective wear.

Stormy seas at Teignmouth

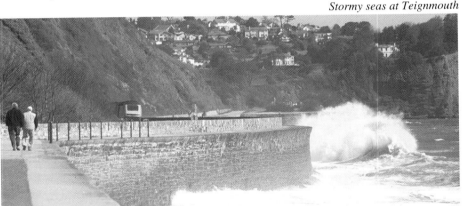

This little book is a chronologically arranged look at specific years, when weather conditions made adverse impact on day-to-day life. It is not a dull, dreary record of meteorological statistics, but tells of some of the consequences of extremes of weather – floods, blizzards, lightning strikes, fireballs, fog, storms and disasters.

Most of the featured reports are from a time before 'global warming', when communications were primitive or non-existent, and when things we take for granted simply weren't around: electricity, central heating, double or triple glazing, insulated homes, four-wheel drives, gritting lorries, lifeboats, air ambulances, trained rescue groups, mobile phones, local radio, television and so on.

To kick things off, here is an undated weather-warning, a hard luck story in the form of an epitaph from a gravestone in North Devon:

Here lies a man who was killed by lightning;
He died when his prospects seemed to be brightening.
He might have cut a flash in this world of trouble,
But the flash cut him, and he lies in the stubble.

3 August 1628 – Brimstone, but No Fire! (and No Rain)

The first anecdote is a reminder of the local nature of thunderstorms. Sitting at the base of the highest part of northern Dartmoor, the town of Okehampton was enjoying some fine weather when John Rattenbury observed that at: ...*about four o' clock in the afternoon, immediately after evening prayer ended at the Church of Okehampton, there being no rain perceived to fall within or near this town, and the streets then being very dry, the water now being called Lede, or the East water, was suddenly risen about some five foot at the East bridge, running more violent than had been usually known, and twas conceived the water did savour and smell of some brimstone.*

21 October 1638 – The Land of Thunder

With the mention of brimstone, that hint of the possible presence of the Devil is taken a step further on Dartmoor, an area sometimes referred to as 'The Land of Thunder'. Widecombe's impressive church of St Pancras was the victim of such a storm when it was struck by a thunderbolt. Legend has it that it was the work of the Devil. It is said that he had been cheated in a game of cards, so was intent on wreaking his revenge on the card-sharp, who was present in this church.

However, that doesn't get any mention in the following account, written the following year, reworded here for easy understanding: *Upon Sunday 21 October last, in the parish church... there fell during Divine Service a strange darkness, increasing more and more, so that the people assembled there could not see to read... and suddenly, in a fearful and lamentable manner, a mighty thundering was heard, like the sound of great cannons, and with terrible strange lightning, greatly amazing and astonishing those that heard and saw it, the darkness increasing yet more, till they could not see one another; the extraordinary lightning came into the church so flaming, that it was filled with fire and smoke, the smell being loathsome, like that of brimstone. Some said they saw a great ball of fire come in through the window and pass through the church, which so scared the whole congregation that most of them fell down into their seats, and some to their knees, some on their faces, and some on top of each other, with a great cry of burning and scalding, all of them giving themselves up for dead.*

The Minister, George Lyde, being in the pulpit, however much he was astonished, yet through God's mercy, was uninjured. Although he wasn't touched, the lightning seized upon his poor wife, fired her ruff and linen next to her body, and her clothes burning many parts of her body. Mistress Ditford, sitting in the pew with her, was also much scalded, but the maid and child sitting by the pew door were unharmed.

Beside, another woman attempting to run from the church was not only burnt but had her flesh torn about her back almost to the very bones. And another woman had her flesh so torn and her body so grievously burnt that she died the same night.

Also Master Hill, a gentleman of good account, sitting in his seat by the chancel, had his head suddenly smitten against the wall, the violence of which killed him, no other hurt being found on his body. His son, sitting beside him, came to no harm.

There was another man, a warrener, whose head was cloven, his skull rent into three pieces, and his brains thrown to the ground whole, and the hair on his head, through the violence of the blow, stuck fast to a pillar or wall of the church; so that he perished most lamentably.

Some other persons were then blasted and burnt, and so grievously scalded and wounded, that since that time they have died... Some had their clothes burnt and their bodies were unhurt, and on the contrary, some had their bodies burnt, whilst their clothes were untouched. But it pleased God yet in the midst of judgement to remember mercy, sparing some and not destroying all. [Well, that's all right, then!]

Also there were some seats in the body of the church which were turned upside down and yet those who sat in them were not hurt. One man going out of the chancel door, his dog running ahead of him was whirled about towards the door and was killed. His master stood back from the door and God preserved him...

Moreover the church, itself, was much torn and defaced by the thunder and lightning. A beam in the midst of the church fell down between the minister and clerk and hurt neither; and an immense stone, near the foundation of the church was torn out and removed. The steeple was much rent and where the church was most rent, there was least harm done, and nobody was injured by wood or stone. However a Manaton girl, who came to see some friends, was killed by a stone...

There were stones thrown from the tower in such amounts that it could have been the work of a hundred men. Also a pinnacle of the tower was thrown down and fell through into the church.

Also the pillar against which the pulpit stood, being recently cleaned, is now black again and sulphery. Furthermore, another man who stood in the chancel, with his faced turned towards the belfry, observed a sudden rising of dust or lime which whirled up, as if caught by a sudden gust of wind, and was blinded for twelve hours but then regained his sight, sustaining no other injuries.

The terrible lightning now past, all the people were in such a maze that nobody spoke a word. After a while, Master Ralph Rouse, stood up, saying, "Neighbours, in the name of God, shall we venture out of the church?" Master Lyde, replied "It is best to make an end of prayers, for it is better to die here than in another place." But they looked about, saw how terribly rent was the church, did not proceed with their devotions and left the church. All this occurred within the church but there were also strange accidents outside of it. There was a bowling alley near the churchyard which was turned into pits and heaps, as if it had been ploughed. At the same time at Brixton, near Plymouth, there fell such hailstones, that for quantity they were judged to be as big as ordinary turkeys' eggs; some of them were five, six or seven ounces in weight...

The village schoolmaster recorded the story for posterity; his version is displayed on four large boards found just inside the entrance to the church.

1703 – All At Sea

Daniel Defoe (1660–1731) is perhaps most famous for his book *Robinson Crusoe*, which was based on a man who once resided at Plymouth. On a journey from London to Land's End, he wrote: *Upon this rock (which was called the Eddystone, from its situation) the famous Mr Winstanley undertook to build a lighthouse for the direction of sailors, and with great art and expedition finished it; which work – considering its height, the magnitude of its building, and the little hold there was by which it was possible to fasten it to the rock – stood to admiration, and bore out many a bitter storm.*

Mr Winstanley often visited, and frequently strengthened, the building, by new works, and was so confident of its firmness and stability that he usually said he only desired to be in it when a storm should happen; for many people had told him it would certainly fall if it came to blow a little harder than ordinary.

But he happened at last to be in it once too often – namely, when that dreadful tempest blew, November 27, 1703. This tempest began on the Wednesday before, and blew with such violence, and shook the lighthouse so much, that, as they told me there, Mr Winstanley would fain have been on shore, and made signals for help; but no boats durst go off to him; and, to finish the tragedy, on the Friday, November 26, when the tempest was so redoubled that it became a terror to the whole nation, the first sight there seaward that the people of Plymouth were presented with in the morning after the storm was the bare Eddystone, the lighthouse being gone; in which Mr Winstanley and all that were with him perished, and were never seen or heard of since. But that which was a worse loss still was that, a few days after, a merchant's ship called the Winchelsea, homeward bound from Virginia, not knowing the Eddystone lighthouse was down, for want of the light that should have been seen, run foul of the rock itself, and was lost with all her lading and most of her men...

There have been several more structures built on the rock since: those of Rudyard, Smeaton (the tower now on Plymouth Hoe), and James Douglas, who built the current Eddystone Lighthouse.

22 August 1768 – A Tamar and Tavy Tempest

In the morning, a tornado flattened an orchard at Bere Ferrers in the Tamar Valley before swirling up one of its major tributaries, the Tavy valley. It passed Tavistock by without causing much mischief, but inflicted immense damage to woods further up the valley. This freak occurrence greatly frightened the villagers of both Peter Tavy and Mary Tavy, on opposite sides of the river. They ran out of their houses to see a large cloud, "like a woolpack", tumble noisily up the valley, violently shaking everything in its wake.

18 January 1775 – A Bridge over Troubled Waters

There was a great flood when the River Exe rose quickly after heavy rain on the high moors of Exmoor. The second Exe Bridge at Exeter endured much damage.The bridge's architect, Mr Dixon, was sacked because it was felt that this new and expensive structure should have been more resilient.

1810 – That Way Inclined

The book *Fair Devon* (1907) noted some of the buildings in and around Barnstaple, in particular the leaning spire of one of its principal places of worship: *The parish church is dedicated to St Peter. The present edifice was consecrated by Bishop Stapeldon in 1318, almost certainly on the site and lines of an older edifice. The leaden spire, which has the appearance of being twisted, being, in fact, inclined to the south, arrests the attention of all visitors. This deflection was caused by a great thunderstorm, which occurred in 1810, expending the whole of its force on church and steeple...*

Also 1810 – 'Devil Water'

The Brook, as it is commonly known, or Dawlish Water, as the map prefers, runs through the heart of the resort and into the sea near the seafront railway station. The stream normally trickles its way to the sea, and is home to some enormous trout and many ducks, geese and black swans.

Its name has been interpreted as meaning 'Devil Water'. This tag has justified itself on many occasions. In mid-November 1810, after a prolonged period of heavy rain on the Haldon Hills, where most of its feeders rise, the torrent was such that a hay cart near Ashcombe, some three miles inland, was lifted, carried along by the river and washed well out to sea. Days later, fishermen spied it floating many miles off the South Devon coast, amazingly still intact.

18 May 1813 – Mayhem in Mid-Devon

As we have seen already, church towers and spires, being invariably the tallest structures, are vulnerable to the elements. This is what happened to one of mid-Devon's quietest villages: *On Wednesday last, about 1 o'clock in the afternoon, the inhabitants of Chulmleigh and its neighbourhood, were visited by the most awful storm of Thunder and Lightning, Hail and Rain, ever remembered by the oldest inhabitant. The Lightning struck out a very large stone, from one of the pinnacles of the tower, which fell on to the roof of the church, and has done considerable damage to it. In less than two hours the rivers overflowed their banks, and deluged the adjoining lands, so deep that in many places not even the hedges could be seen. The bridges were rendered impassable; so that the Mail could not return to Barnstaple from Chulmleigh, till two o' clock on Thursday morning. The potato and barley fronds have suffered greatly. In many places, and to a considerable extent, the earth is carried away, and heaps of rubbish left in its stead.*

That same evening, about ten o' clock, Mr Shute of Dolton, a very respectable man, was drowned in attempting to pass over Newnham bridge, leading over the river Taw, at the western extremity of Chulmleigh parish.

27 July 1813 – "Goodness Gracious…"

About two months later, it was Exeter's turn to suffer extreme violence from the hand of Nature: *During the thunderstorm which pervaded Exeter and its vicinity last Tuesday afternoon, a ball of fire fell upon one of the stables of the Cavalry barracks on the northern side of the city. It struck on the ridge of the roof, dislodged the slates from the laths, for about two feet round, and entering struck a cross beam, which it broke, and spent itself on the stable floor. It was seen distinctly, falling, after an explosion of thunder, and heard to burst like a shell. – There was no stone, or other concretion, found, except a little dust or soot, such as remains from an explosion of gun-powder; nor was there any thing on the long low roof on which it fell, that possessed any peculiar attraction. It appeared to have been thrown there by the spontaneous impulse that kindled it. Happily, it did no other damage than we have described.*

For the record, having housed the Ministry of Defence in the latter years of the 20th century, the barracks have been converted into a residential housing development known as 'Horseguards'.

Early January 1814 – "In the Bleak Mid-winter"

The snow which began to fall in this neighbourhood on the evening of Monday 10th instant, and continued falling till the afternoon of the following day, is believed by our aged neighbours to have formed a heavier mass, than has fallen in this quarter, within the same space of time, since the hard winter of 1777–78. Intelligent observers of natural phenomena estimate it at a depth of 16 inches; but, as it was borne along by a strong gale of wind it drifted into heaps in some places

of incredible magnitude; and, acquiring cohesion by freezing as it fell, it wreathed itself from tree and house-tops, in pendant forms of infinite variety and beauty. Throughout Tuesday, the greater part of our shops were shut up, and some of our streets rendered almost impassable; while the roads diverging from Exeter, were in many parts absolutely blocked up. The London mails throughout the week, have lost from twelve to 18 hours each of their usual time, owing chiefly to the great accumulation of snow at a place called Longbury (or Longbreedy) Hut, near Bridport in Dorset, where the coaches have been stopped, and the bags sent forward on horses. The Bath mail coach has kept to within an hour or two of its time, throughout the week. The mails from the North of Devon have lost time on an average of twelve hours per day. The mail direct through Launceston, for Falmouth, which started last Tuesday morning, was stopped (we understand) somewhere about Launceston, Five Lanes or the Jamaica Inn; and, up to yesterday afternoon, there has been no exchange of letters by that line of road. About three o' clock, the Falmouth mails arrived here, on horses; having been brought from Bodmin to Launceston on men's shoulders. Neither has there been any passing over Dartmoor to Princetown. The heights of Haldon (5 miles from Exeter on the Plymouth road) were also impassable. Two fish-carts caught there on Tuesday, were abandoned; their drivers glad to get off with their horses. Coaches and Chaises which attempted that road, from Exeter, were compelled to return. The mails sent hence on Friday last, on three horses, for Plymouth, were forced back again. On Saturday the accumulated mails for Plymouth, and for Cornwall were sent from Foale's Hotel on 8 horses and succeeded on crossing Haldon; – 15 or 16 horses came in here on the same day, with mails from Plymouth. On Friday there was another pretty smart shower of snow; but on Saturday it thawed, and continued to do so till yesterday when it froze again...

We have only heard of one life lost in the snow: a private of the East Devon Militia, coming to Exeter on furlough, was found up to his chin, on Haldon, frozen to death. He had about £15 in his pockets...

Among those who, at this season of extraordinary hardship on the poor, having enjoyed the luxury of doing good, Lord Rolle caused a fine fat bullock and six fat sheep to be distributed on Wednesday last to the poor of the parish of St Giles, round his Lordship's seat of Stevenstone, near Torrington; – and next day (being that of Thanksgiving) his Lordship, as Rector of Torrington, opened a subscription, which was liberally followed up by the respectable inhabitants, and expended in regaling their labouring and poor neighbours. After Divine Service, two fat bullocks were divided up, and a sheep roasted whole; which, with due proportions of bread and beer, regaled a thousand persons. The excellent band of the Local Militia attended, playing "God Save the King", and other national airs. In the evening there were bonfires, and fireworks let off at the Castle. A select party of Ladies and Gentlemen spent the evening at the town-hall. The bells rang out the day at Little Torrington: all was joy and thankfulness...

About four o' clock in the afternoon of Sunday the 9th of January, a small boat was observed by the fishermen and inhabitants of the shores in Start Bay (between Dartmouth and the Start) drifting towards the land. As the boat approached the shore, the two men were distinctly seen in

8

it, steering with an oar. As, however, the sea was very rough, it was impossible to render them any assistance, until the boat approached the land, when a tremendous wave lifted it near 20 feet high, and dashed it to pieces on the shore. One of the men, by twisting a rope which was attached to the boat round his arm, was thrown so high upon the beach, that by the active exertions of the fishermen and inhabitants (one of whom risked his life on the occasion) he was dragged on shore, alive, but much swollen and bruised. The other poor fellow was seen struggling in the waves, and one of the dogs for which this coast is famous, had actually seized him by the collar, when another tremendous wave overwhelmed, and, by its recoil, carried both away. The dog, after a short interval, was seen again buffeting the waves, and at length arrived safe on the shore; but the poor man found an end to his sufferings in the watery grave. It appears that the men were marines, belonging to his majesty's gun-brig "Swinger" and that on Friday the 7th instant, about seven o' clock in the evening, they, in company with another marine, rowed off the shore to join their ship then living in Portland Roads; but not being able to reach her, and being numbed by the cold, they were driven by the gale from Portland Roads to Start Bay, a distance of 18 leagues; after having been exposed to the inclemency of the weather and the dreadful snow storm on Friday night, for 10 hours; in consequence of which one had already died in the boat. The name of the survivor is James Webb, corporal of the marines; and of the dead, John Hutchinson and Richard Saunders, private marines.

25 January 1814 – A Gentleman of the Road

The week that has passed since our last publication, has been one of considerable embarrassment to a very large proportion of every order of the community; but more especially to commercial persons, whose communications with their bankers have been stopped – to travellers , who have been detained upon the road...

The weather underwent a sudden transition on Wednesday night, from rain, and the thaw which had prevailed for some days, to a return of frost and another heavy fall of snow...

Four mail coaches which left Exeter for Plymouth were stopped for some days at the foot of Haldon, where three or four score of men were employed on the Thursday, Friday and Saturday last, clearing the snow with shovels; and where they dug out two horses, still alive, whose riders had happily escaped on foot back to Chudleigh. We visited the summit of Haldon on Saturday; from whence, the dreary wastes of snow extending over all the surrounding hills and vales – except where the rugged tors of eastern Dartmoor, swept by the storm, rose black and grim, like rocks emerging from the ocean – presented a scene of gloomy grandeur, difficult to describe...

Whiteway-house, adjoining Haldon, the truly hospitable mansion of Montague Parker esq, has been, for a fortnight past, the asylum of the rich and poor, high and low. This gentleman employed his servants to look for the many travellers, who might be stopped by the impenetrable heaps of snow, or lose their way in this quarter, and conduct them to his house; where they have been fed, and lodged, in great numbers, and received every other comfort and relief that their cases required, with a degree of generosity and liberality, which will reflect lasting honour on his name.

Several weeks later the *Western Luminary* reflected on the consequences of the previous months extreme conditions: *Among the effects of the late severe winter, was the death of a great number of young colts upon the heights of Exmoor and Dartmoor. A gentleman who lately traversed the moors, assures us, that he counted above twenty skeletons. Another effect of the same cause, is the vast reduction of small birds; which it is observable are much less numerous in gardens and orchards, this spring, than in former seasons: a circumstance which augurs well for the approaching crops of fruit if the advantage be not counteracted by the want of their usual services in destroying grubs and insects.*

18 May 1815 – A Tale of Woe

The day started with a fine sunny morning, a perfect day for a wedding at Otterton church. After the ceremony the newlyweds joined their friends on a boat trip to Sidmouth. Here they spent some time celebrating in a pub before heading home. Alas, a sudden squall caused their boat to capsize in Lyme Bay. The bride, five other girls and a young lad were all drowned. The bridegroom survived the tragedy and later married again.

June 1825 – A Kingsbridge Calamity

The vulnerability of tall objects standing up above others is highlighted again in this story from the South Hams, where the church spire was nearer to Heaven than was good for it. *During the thunderstorm on the 22 ult, the electric fluid about 2 p.m., struck the spire of Kingsbridge Church, and descending the iron work of the weather cock, passed by a wire from the belfry into the interior of the church, and in a zigzag direction through it, making its exit over the communion table. The mischief done is considerable, and about 16 feet of the spire has been obliged to be taken down. The rain at the time fell so heavily that the streets were impassable, and many houses were not merely inundated, but the waters made a complete sweep through them. Roofs of houses, chimneys, &c also sustained injury.*

2 February 1851 – The Shape of Things to Come?

Long before the term 'global warming' was coined, a local man reflected on the previous month's weather and noted that: *Not a flake of snow fell on the Forest of Dartmoor... not the oldest man living on the Moor recollects the like before.*

12 February 1853 – Lost in a White-out

Two years almost to the day from the previous report, things were back to normal. Many reckon that February is a more extreme month than January in terms of harsh weather. For Joseph Penton, Patrick Carlin and George Driver, all soldiers with the 7th Fusiliers, this proved to be the case, as they lost their lives in a snowdrift when attempting to reach Princetown from the direction of Dousland. This memorial is found by a wall in the churchyard.

February 1855 – The Devil's Footprints

The Devil normally scoots about undetected, but even he can't avoid leaving evidence of his presence in the snow. Such was the case, it is alleged, one winter's morning when there was considerable evidence of his presence. A continuous trail, estimated to run for more than a hundred miles over hill and dale, was there for all to see – well, those brave or foolish enough to venture out of doors.

When some folk had scraped the ice from inside the windows of their humble abodes, and ventured forth into the white world, they noticed a row of hoof-marks forming a single line. It was later realised that this crossed Woodbury Common twice, and led to a point just beyond Totnes in the south of the county. Those who followed the footprints discovered that, on reaching obstacles such as houses, or even mansions, instead of detouring around, they went up and over them. Naturally there was much conjecture to what or to whom they belonged. The line was too convincing to be a hoax and theories included some fanciful notions: a one-legged abominable kangaroo; the Great Bustard (*Otis tarda* to Latin-lovers); a two-legged donkey! Others looked to the supernatural for an explanation – and the Devil became suspect number one. Although most hoof-prints could be identified, nobody had taken the Devil's gait before; the $8^{1}/_{2}$ inches gap suggested a lively little fellow.

The *News of the World* and *The Times* covered the story, but the *London Illustrated News* featured it in greatest detail. All the reports noted that the route carefully avoided Exeter, where the Cathedral was probably a suitable deterrent to ward off this evil character.

Woolmer's *Exeter & Plymouth Gazette* was also on hand, but carefully managed to avoid any mention of the Devil by name. Dawlish, famed for its mild climate, also felt the icy blast and its paper indulged in the following speculation.

The weather during the past week has been intensely cold... Dawlish readers will find... many curious particulars relating to the extraordinary foot marks which have caused so much excitement on both sides of the Exe estuary.

In connection with the above 'mysteries' we have received the following particulars from our Dawlish correspondent – "His footprints were traced through the greater part of the town. They resembled somewhat those of a donkey, but, to add to the effect of the mystery, it was rumoured in some instances they were "cloven". So great was the excitement produced by the reports which got abroad that a party of tradesmen and others armed themselves with guns and bludgeons, and spent the greater part of the day in tracing the foot-prints. From the church-yard they proceeded to the grounds of Luscombe and Dawlish Water, and thence to Oaklands. At length, after a long and weary search, they returned as wise as they set out. Some considered that the footprints were those of a large bird from a foreign shore, and others believed that they were those of a kangaroo or wolf, or some other beast escaped from a travelling menagerie."

The greatest mystery was that in no place could there be traced more than two impressions, which were about 16 inches apart. It will be remembered that we had a heavy fall of snow, about 4 inches deep, on the previous evening...

Churchgoers to Dawlish's parish church sought out the vicar to ask him how they could protect themselves against the beast. Some years later, the vicar's daughter, Henrietta Fursdon, wrote: *The footprints appeared during the night... They looked as if they had been made by the foot of a goat and continued in a never-ending line into the distance. I clearly remember how I saw the footprints and... was overwhelmed by fear... Yet not only we children were frightened, the servants refused to go out after dark even to lock the gates.*

The footprints formed a continuous line of about 110 miles, travelling from East Devon into South Devon, and 'visited' 17 towns and villages along the way.

January 1866 – The Great Tempest

Written within living memory after this disaster, under the heading "The Cyclone or January Gale in Torbay", this harrowing account appeared in *Brixham in Devonia*: *On the evening of January 10th, and the morning of January 11th, 1866, a disaster unprecedented in Torbay, took place, for not less than 60 vessels were wrecked, and upwards of 100 lives lost.*

There were at this time 94 vessels at anchor here, windbound; these vessels were steamers, large ships, colliers, coasters, &c, of various nationalities.

During the day a strong gale blew from the South-west, with thick snow, which at 9 p.m. backened to South; then, suddenly to South-east, and finally to North-east, from which quarter it blew with hurricane force. All the vessels were, therefore, caught in a death-trap; a few of them by slipping their cables, managed to weather the Berry Head, and get into open sea; but all the others dragged their anchors, or parted their cables and drove ashore, with the exception of one or two that managed to get to Harbour. The Inner Harbour of Brixham was already crammed with trawlers, which had come in during the day, but there were about 50 at anchor at their moorings in the Outer Harbour. To make matters worse, the night was pitch dark and rain fell in torrents.

The end of the Breakwater was swept away by the huge seas that broke over it, carrying away the Lighthouse that acted as a guide to the weary mariner, to pilot him to the harbour; and in its place a huge beacon fire was kept alight all the night on the Pier Head to attract the attention of the sailors. Two schooners – the Tangerine, of Brixham, and the Florence Nightingale – entered the harbour safely, but the Wild Rose, an English barque, and the Leonie, an Italian, in running for the harbour ran foul of some trawlers, and came to grief at the back of the Pier. The former vessel dragged in the fishing smack Grace, and the latter brought with her the Briton, also a trawler.

The Lively, Spy, and Forerunner, three trawlers, came ashore at the same time and place. The excitement on the Pier and on the Quays at this time was intense, as the piercing cries of the unfortunate seamen, calling for aid to save them from a fearful death, by being crushed and mangled between the wreckage, penetrated the air, and were heard above the howling of the wind on this fearful night; but thanks to Him who holds the sea in the hollow of His hand, not a single life was lost from among all the vessels that were stranded at this spot.

The trawler Salem came ashore at Oxen Cove, and her crew of four hands saved themselves by swinging ashore with a rope from the masthead, and in less than five minutes after they had left her she was smashed to atoms.

The crews of all these vessels were rescued by being hauled up over the pier by lines thrown from above, and fastened around them; or by climbing the rigging and dropping off from the yards into the arms of the fishermen who lined the pier in hundreds to rescue the perishing, in spite of the danger they ran of being killed by the rigging, blocks and spars, that fell about their heads. In a very short time these vessels were shattered to matchwood.

At daylight, the crew of the trawler Colonel Buller, which was riding at her moorings in the outer harbour, got into their small boat with a view to pulling ashore, and shortly after letting go the painter they were seen to drive across one of the swing chains of the trawler, which threw the boat and its occupants high into the air. The boat was thereby broken up, and all three of these poor fellows were drowned within sight of their relatives, who were powerless to render any assistance.

The names of the fishermen were Samuel Crocker, the Skipper, William Bucknell, 3rd hand, and S. Blackmore, cook. The second hand, James Memery, was put on board a strange vessel the previous day, to pilot her to a neighbouring seaport, and thereby, in all probability, escaped the fate of his shipmates.

At noon on the 11th there was so much wreckage outside that some of the fishermen walked on planks and other parts of the vessels from the end of the pier to the Paint Works. Floating on the water were tons of flour, lard, casks of wine, &c.

Many vessels foundered in the bay. From Brixham to Goodrington the shore was one mass of wreckage, and the remains of many seamen were found along the coast, wrapped up in canvas, and brought ashore for interment.

At Broadsands nine vessels were ashore, whilst nine others left their remains just to the Northward of this point. In Churston Cove a large ship went to pieces, and of crew of ten hands, four only were saved.

A schooner was at this spot actually carried by the sea into a field above, the whole of her crew being thereby landed on terra firma.

Devon's Wild & Wicked Weather

To the southward of this point a brigantine, loaded with coffee beans, drove ashore, her crew being rescued by a number of fishermen on the rocks. The captain of the vessel was heard to say after he had been saved "Thank God, we are saved, but O! my poor coffee which I have been so far to fetch."

Three vessels went ashore at the back of the breakwater, their crews being all rescued by those on shore who plunged into the sea with lines fastened around them and swam off to their aid; the whole crew of one of those vessels was saved in this manner. One brig ran on the beach inside the breakwater, where the sea was comparatively smooth. An English barque named the Princess Beatrice came ashore at Dewdneys' Cove, and was afterwards got off with but little damage.

All through the night, and up to noon the next day, vessels were being driven on the rocks along the bay, and people were hurrying to and fro to the work of rescue; for no sooner had a number of seamen been saved from one part of the bay, than the crowd engaged in the work were called upon to render assistance in another place. All through the terrible night the people on shore acted with noble generosity, by opening their doors to the shipwrecked mariners, and providing them with food and clothing. The fishermen's wives and daughters on the Quay were up all night attending to their wants, by preparing warm food and clothing for each as they were brought ashore.

The next day the old Assembly Rooms (the site of which is now the Conservative Club and other buildings) was converted into a home for the sailors...

This terrible disaster caused a profound impression, and meetings for the relief of the widows and orphans were held...

Later in the same year some of those who had distinguished themselves by heroic and other deeds in this great gale, were handsomely rewarded. Christopher Bartlett, a boatman, who was lowered over a dangerous cliff at Oxen Cove to a wreck, by which means he was instrumental in rescuing many lives, received a suitable reward, and a little girl, named Mary Putt, who held the lantern the while, was also rewarded. The Board of Trade awarded four bronze medals to C. Bartlett, Ezekiah Curtis, Edwin Barter, and C. W. Wyatt. Soon after this the citizens of Exeter collected money for a lifeboat for Torbay, and on the 10th of November she was brought here, and launched into the harbour from Cayme's Slip. She was named the City of Exeter, and was launched by the Mayor of that city.

Soon after the gale representations were made and petitions sent to the Board of Trade, praying for the construction of a Breakwater across Torbay. Sir Laurence Palk also introduced the subject to the House of Commons, but with no practical result.

1866 – They're Up…

And there's more! Sarah Prideaux Fox, of Kingsbridge, wrote this in 1874: *A lime kiln just here was for a long time noticeable on account of a noble Wych elm, growing quite through a side wall, and spreading its graceful branches all over the front of the kiln. It was the only specimen of this particular kind of elm that we knew of anywhere in the neighbourhood, but it was laid low by a fearful gale which occurred in January 1866, and did much damage in this vicinity. At Wallingford the gale seems to have been felt by its greatest force – the wind taking the line of the valley. There are, or rather were, in that valley, several hedges full of fine elm trees, and one after another of these were completely swept away, the trees lying along in regular rows, as if they had been felled with an axe. There were altogether one hundred and four trees prostrated in this valley alone.*

1876 – Letting Nature Take its Course!

A local expert, Mr Appleton, since 1855 had been studying the movements of beach materials at Westward Ho! He noted that the storms and seas took a heavy toll on the Pebble Ridge, the west end and the adjoining ground: so much so that the new golf clubhouse (erected and furnished at great expense) was endangered. In front of the clubhouse was a piece of ground belonging to the premises, extending 70 feet from the building, and beyond that was a road about 20 feet wide. The storms of the previous winter (1875/76) had completely washed away the road, and brought down the wall enclosing the club ground. Destruction was also going on to the west of the clubhouse.

In 1877 Mr Appleton was again called in and said that underlying the ridge there was a subsoil of peat and very tenacious clay. If protection was not given to this, he advised, the Pebble Ridge would come down, and a serious breach would take place that would admit the sea at the westward end and allow a channel to be formed across the furrows to Appledore, flooding at high water the whole of the Burrows.

Mr Appleton recommended groynes and flank defences, but nothing came of it, and his report was scarcely dry when the clubhouse and ground went, and the ridge was driven far along the Burrows. The weakness of the ridge was attributed to the large number of stones taken for roadmaking and building. Also, an old custom of 'pot-walloping', whereby the displaced stones were placed back onto the Pebble Ridge by 'pot-wallopers', had been abandoned.

And so it goes on, Man and Nature jockeying with each other to keep the defences up or knock them down.

1880s – Storm-tossed Seas

This is part of a report from the 1880s, following a few days of stormy, wet weather when many places were inundated. *A large amount of damage, caused by extremely high tides, was done along the coast, in particular at Dawlish's station where the side on the down-line took a pounding. The mail-train down from the north was compelled to run between Dawlish and Teignmouth through an almost continuous sheet of water of flying spray coming over the wall. Several windows on the sea side of the carriages were smashed and one passenger received a head-cut from flying glass and another an injury to the hand. The carriages received large quantities of sea water and the luggage vans were completely swamped. The tide was extraordinarily high. Fortunately no serious damage was caused to the line.*

4 May 1880 – Taking the Plunge

This delightfully fine day was when the GWR started running their early morning cheap excursion bathing trains from Exeter to the coast. The opening day of the 'sea-bathing season' was celebrated by a swift and highly invigorating swim. The keenest participants – there were several hundred – changed into their costumes as the train approached Dawlish. So enthusiastic were some to be first into the water that they could hardly wait for the train to grind to a halt before they were off into the briny. For this macho example of derring-do they were rewarded at the resort's Royal Albert Hotel with a slap-up breakfast, generously paid for by the wealthy Charlie Ross. In later years he switched to the Grand Hotel for the post-swim feast.

January 1881 – Brass Monkeys

Boy, it was cold! There are those who believe that the blizzards of 1881 were worse than the famed "Great Blizzard of 1891", which we will get to later. Devon was not singled out for the icy blast; the effects were felt across a much wider area. Although Hell didn't freeze over, it was possible to walk across the sea from Denmark to Sweden! The icy blast came from the east with unrelenting force. It deposited a constant snow depth of over three feet across the Isle of Wight, thus making it, in another sense, a true Isle of White! Conditions were even more extreme on Dartmoor where there was a recorded blanket depth of four feet, with drifts up to 30 feet high.

The railways, so important in getting around the country at that time, were thus beaten by the weather for days on end. Apart from the volume of snow to be dumped from the heavens, the ferocious wind meant the chill factor reached levels that stopped people dead in their tracks – literally. When the weather began to weaken its grip, a number of shepherds tending their flocks on exposed high ground were found bolt upright, like frozen statues, their sheep having suffered a similar fate.

December 1884 – No Salvation!

A gale raged at Bideford with the greatest violence and did much damage. A new hall erected by Mr Shute in the Market-place was completely wrecked. The building was destined for the use of the Salvation Army, and had only been opened as "barracks" the previous evening, the event being celebrated by a public tea.

About six o'clock on Saturday evening, when the storm was at its highest, the roof of the structure was torn off and pitched into an adjoining yard. Shortly afterwards the whole of the end wall crashed down bodily into the interior of the building, smashing into the floor and wrecking the hall. The Salvationists will consequently have to find some other place in which to hold their meetings for the time being.

July 1890 – Cell Block H₂O

According to William Crossing, the elements were wild in the extreme: *The great thunderstorm... will not soon be forgotten, particularly on the western side of Dartmoor... The long clapper at Bairdown was unfortunately washed away... a portion of Merivale Bridge being carried away,*

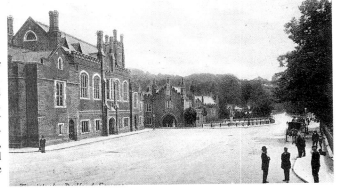

and Ward Bridge, widely celebrated for its picturesqueness, was entirely demolished...

Meanwhile, a drama was unfolding in the cells of Tavistock's police station. These lay below ground level in Bedford Square. As the banks of the nearby River Tavy burst, an extremely worried prisoner, watching the water level rise in his cell, had to be rescued.

1891 – The Great Blizzard

This began as most folks thought the worst rigours of winter were past. February had been unusually mild: spring flowers were beginning to emerge. What followed was most unseasonal. The wind suddenly grew in strength during the afternoon of Monday 9 March; with it came vast amounts of snow that whited out the county and affected life for six weeks. For four unremitting days, force 10 winds raged and mountains of snow piled up.

Here are just a few of the 'stories' from that terrifying time.

At the former Raglan Barracks in Plymouth, the troops were subjected to the terrifying ordeal of the wind blowing all the windows in, with several people being cut by flying shards of glass.

A more amusing scene presented itself on Mutley Plain. As the wind howled down the street, and the snow drifted into deep mounds, two portly gentlemen debated whether or not to try to cross the road. Gathering their courage, they went for broke. Despite their bulk, the wind bowled them off their feet and continued to carry them along the road. As they rolled over, layers of snow quickly built up around each of them, so that by the time they eventually came to a sudden halt, they looked, to all the world, like living snowmen. When one of them gathered his wits, he confided to his friend that his biggest fear had been the distinct possibility that he would have been rolled over and crushed by his pal. Abominable!

The Dartmouth–Modbury road passes over Gara Bridge to rise to California Cross, where the pub is, not surprisingly, the California Inn. It was the scene, more than a century ago, where wayfarers were marooned in far from warm conditions.

This is how a passenger described the journey by stage coach, just two years before the railway linked Kingsbridge with the main line at Brent (Wrangaton), as the Great Blizzard began to exert its influence over the South Hams landscape.

Having been at Salcombe on business we left the King's Arms Hotel, Kingsbridge, on Monday, March 9th, at 5 p.m., in Foale's 'bus for train at Kingsbridge Road Station, 9½ miles away, myself and seven others, in a conveyance only fit to hold six… It was a case of close stowage and warmth, but as at starting it was blowing hard from the north-east, with sleet, and the air bitterly cold, the warmth we could well appreciate. In due course we passed the village of Loddiswell where it was… bitterly cold, and sleeting, We had only got a mile from Loddiswell when the 'bus stopped with a jerk; a snow-man, or a shape-less mass of snow, with a human being in the middle, appeared. The sudden rush of outer air froze the perspiration-covered 'bus and ourselves into ice in a second. The driver then proceeded to explain why he couldn't or wouldn't go on but the passengers, to a man, insisted and offered extra remuneration for him to do so. Against his better judgement he continued. But we seemed to have gone only a few hundred yards further when it stopped again and the driver once more appeared, and said, "It's no use, gentlemen; we are stuck; I can do nothing further, and now there is no possibility of going back the mile we are from Loddiswell; as that road is also blocked by the snow-drift, so you have either to stop where you are until the storm is over or assistance sent, or struggle through the snow on foot to the California Inn, 1½ miles ahead." Out we gentlemen tumbled from the 'bus up to our knees at once in snow, and blowing a terrific gale from the north-east, with the snow falling in a dense mass, making breathing difficult. We then found the cause of the trouble not to be the driver, for right in front of the horses was a solid mass of snow-drift eight feet high, caused by the snow being driven across the fields through a gateway to the opposite road-wall, completely filling the road. So there we were in 18 inches of snow, barred both in front and rear by a solid wall of eight feet high, or the height of the hedges. We held counsel, and quickly made up our minds to force a passage for ourselves on foot to the California Inn...We had to leave the poor driver to get assistance at the nearest farm for his horses, as we could do nothing for him. By avoiding roads, which were impassable, taking to the fields, and clambering hedges, under the guidance of one of the passengers, who lived a half-mile from our destination, fighting our way inch by inch, we eventually reached the California Inn – an ordinary country roadside inn, with very little

accommodation, and no other houses near. We were, however, glad of any shelter after our terrible buffeting. They were nearly snowed up themselves, no entry at the front door could be observed, so we had to go around the back. We found several other snowed-up travellers from the surrounding places in the same predicament as ourselves, all being caught by the extreme suddenness of the storm. The good landlord and landlady did all they could for us, but our numbers astounded them, for at a place like that over twenty extra guests cannot be catered for at once. After being supplied with tea and plenty of ham and eggs in a spare room the Inn afforded, we had, perforce to make up our minds to stay the night. And what a night it was. The wind shrieking around the house, exposed as it was in an open moor-land-like country. At daybreak we looked out on a grand sight. The whole country covered in deep snow, the roads being full from hedge-top to hedge-top, and the fields covered to an average depth of three feet, and still snowing and blowing a hurricane. The stage-coach was stuck in snow until Thursday 19th March, ten days later! If you visit the pub, which was first established in 1756, you may care to look out for a mention of Foale's in some of the ironwork outside, and a stage coach.

Rail travellers, in those places that had railway lines, fared little better. There were numerous tales of passengers being marooned on stranded trains. In North Devon the evening Ilfracombe to Barnstaple service came to a halt some 200 yards from Mortehoe Station, on a high point of the line. Here a 20-foot snowdrift engulfed it, so that only the chimney was visible protruding above the 'snow-line'. Fortunately, despite a white-out, the passengers managed to reach Mortehoe Station, where cups of coffee helped to thaw them out.

Meanwhile, a telegraph message was sent down to Barnstaple to tell of the travellers' plight. A relief train was prepared, with 20 railway workers on board, and this set off at about 11 p.m. from the North Devon capital. Despite the good intention, the train never made it to Mortehoe,

as it suffered the same fate as the earlier train. Once more those on board had to abandon the train, and were obliged to battle their way through the blizzard on foot to reach Mortehoe.

The nearest available accommodation was the Fortescue Hotel. Inevitably all manner of wayfarers had to 'hole-up' here until the conditions improved. Bed space was at such a premium that some people decided to rough it in the stationmaster's office, or even the signal box!

However, hospitality was in short supply at South Brent, on the (not so) Great Western Railway; one passenger on a four-day journey from London to Plymouth, cited his 'bitter experience': *Most of us put up in the station. We were without any refreshments, but the station master went to bed at his usual time, not even asking us to have a cup of tea or coffee… Next day we descended on South Brent… The inhabitants put up everything to famine prices… and some establishments refused to serve us at all…We returned to the station through the great drifts of snow, and cooked bloaters in the waiting room. For the next three days there was nothing to do but smoke and talk…*

There was also peril on the sea. The gale force winds, and abominable conditions of no visibility, meant that those sailing close to the mountainous cliffs along the coast between Lynmouth and Ilfracombe were at enormous risk. The 300-ton brigantine *Ethel,* with a crew of six, foundered under High Vere Point, or Highveer Point as the OS map now would have it.

Rather than risk trying to land at Heddon's Mouth, just yards away, they launched the lifeboat and rowed for several hours to reach the safe haven of Combe Martin, about six miles to the west. Here they were spotted by the coastguards, who rushed to help them come ashore, chilled to the bone after their ordeal beneath the towering coastline.

Less fortunate were the great number of animals slain by the blizzard; a number of sheep succumbed to nature's 'deep freezer' rather than a man-made one. However, there was the occasional tale of innovation and adaptation. A pig farmer, whose sty was buried well beneath the drifting snow, managed to forge an access from above. He climbed down from the icy surface, using a ladder, and thus managed to look after his pigs in their cosy 'igloo'.

A Braunton lad had a lucky escape. He had been out gathering seaweed to fertilise his strip on the Braunton Great Field, a place which still has this ancient form of land-divided cultivation. Young Mitchell was caught out at the water's edge when the storm took hold. Despite his valiant efforts to offload his 'cargo', his small, heavily laden boat began to sink in the turbulent, icy waters of Bideford (or Barnstaple) Bay. As he floated helplessly, fate offered him a hand: a wooden handcart, or barrow, bobbed by. Grabbing hold of it bought him a few precious moments until a boat came by. A few more minutes and he would have perished.

An old lady living on her own in a remote cottage on the edge of the moors near Tavistock was not so fortunate. She died, but the local undertakers, who were doing a 'good trade', could not get to her for about a week. When they eventually reached the cottage, they made their way up the narrow staircase, with a wicked right-angled turn, and found the frozen corpse laid out on the bed. Unfortunately she was so rigid that their efforts to get her down the stairs and around the corner failed miserably. There was no alternative. They opened the window, and carefully tossed her corpse out onto the snow some feet below. The problem had been solved, albeit in a somewhat undignified way.

24 February 1906 – Going Nowhere Fast

"Equal in intensity to that of 1891, but not of such long duration" was how one local expert described the events. The following report shows the gritty determination of those charged with delivering services to do their best in the face of adversity: *The little village of Princetown has been completely cut off from civilisation – excepting, fortunately, telegraphic communication – for a couple of days. With difficulty the 6.55 p.m. train from Plymouth reached here on Monday night in the teeth of a gale. Mr Higman, the stationmaster, thereupon wired to the officials at Plymouth asking them to send on a snow plough. This was done, but ere the heavy engine could not get through; an engine drawing ten empty granite trucks had come on as far as Johnson's cutting, where the whole lay firmly embedded in a drift, estimated in some parts to be 20ft deep. Gangs of labourers were despatched from head-quarters to clear the line, but it was not until mid-day to-day (Wednesday) that the carriages could be backed down into the Royal Oak siding. Although four engines and steam ploughs were continually at work, it was not until nearly four o'clock that the line was practically cleared…*

In order to bring up the mails Mr W. Tooker and three rural postmen – Messrs Hannaford, Lucas and Pengelly – bravely set out to walk to Yelverton on Tuesday. Had not the Postmaster been well acquainted with the Moor, it is to be feared some accident would have happened. As

it was, when the party reached Doublewaters, Pengelly had to be fished out of a drift into which he had sank up to his neck. From Stenlake to Goatstone Hill the snow had drifted across the road to a depth of eighteen feet. When they got to Peak Hill, the worst part of their journey, they found huge drifts level with the tree tops. They safely reached Dousland in about three hours. Returning home ere daylight faded, they brought three small bags of letters. It was a most trying experience and the men were quite exhausted on their arrival at Princetown. On Tuesday morning seven convicts, under transfer from Dartmoor to London, were marched to Princetown Railway Station, but as the train could not run they were sent back again. To-day two of them, whose term has expired, were sent to Tavistock in charge of the principal warder...

During the past few days the Moor has presented a sublime spectacle. The grand old tors, completely covered with their mantle of white, reflecting back the occasional gleams of sunshine, seemed to look down on varied scenes. At one moment all was calm, and the snowflakes fell quite lazily; then the wind howled, and the snow was driven hither and thither, lashed into fury by the fierce hurricane.

Gangs of convicts have been clearing the roads to-day. Near the Prison gates the snowdrifts were about 15 feet high, rendering it difficult for the duty officers to get to and fro...

9 July 1907 – "Raindrops Keep Falling on My Head"

The following report reveals a certain stiff-upper-lip 'Britishness' of attitude towards the elements. All involved in arranging the following ceremony hoped for a nice day. After all, it was July – but it was also Okehampton!

In some of the less hardy parts of the country a day's rain would be calculated to spoil any open-air festivities. Not so at Okehampton, where what most people would regard as a steady downpour is looked upon as a mere Dartmoor drizzle, certainly not sufficient to keep folks indoors or to quench their ardour in the slightest. Flaunting the sullen skies with bright-hued flags and evergreen-decked poles, the inhabitants of the hill-encircled moorland town yesterday entered into possession of their beautiful park with joyful spirits, cheered the generous donor, Mr Sydney Simmons, with full-throated gratitude, and greeted the Lord Mayor of London with echoing "Hurrahs" wherever he made his appearance in the rain-soaked streets. That the thoroughfares were crowded and that optimism prevailed were matters of wonderment; never were ceremonies conducted under less favourable climatic conditions. True, in the early morning the sun bathed the moors in golden light, but, alas! only to withdraw behind ominous banks of cloud, that before midday dropped their burden of unwelcome moisture. Thence onward the rain never ceased to fall. But everybody, from the Lord Mayor to holiday-making errand boys, triumphed over the depressing atmosphere. Sir William Treloar was, as usual, the veritable embodiment of good spirits. Clad in his gorgeous robes of office, he held high his smiling face, and was an infectious source of good spirits. His fellow Mayors of Devonshire trod in his footsteps with imitative light-heartedness, and the crowds that watched the progress of the civic dignitaries laughed and cheered as heartily as if under skies of the brightest blue.

With such functions as the presentation of the freedom to the Lord Mayor and Mr Sydney Simmons, and the reception and luncheon, the rain did not, of course, interfere, but the opening of the park and the other outdoor festivities were considerably abbreviated. Speeches from the rain-soaked dais were brief, but admirably to the point, and after the opening of the gate of the park the Lord Mayor contented himself with a glimpse of the beautiful pleasure ground, the intended circuit being too much of an ordeal for even Sir William Treloar ...

March 1915

In the worldly-wise words of one of my former great geography lecturers of the late 1960s, Mr Fred Davey: "When the east wind blows, the mini-skirt goes!" How right he was!

SOUTH MOLTON – On Sunday every tree and upright thing did a profound, long bow to the west. There was a black east wind, the coldest this winter, before which even evergreens lost hope and drooped. Sheep stood still in the fields with a white ruffle on their backs and bleated that their bones were aching. Instead of running races and dancing round hillocks, the lambs huddled together in the starkest corner and looked stupid. It was a bitter day. There was every appearance of a fall of snow but none came.

Exceptional as the cold was in the open, in the streets it was worse. The houses served as a channel for the wind, and grit from the road stung one's face. Churchgoers turned up storm-collars and (wiping tears from their blue cheeks) admitted that the weather was 'fresh.' If too numbed to replace the handkerchief in their pocket they carried it in helplessly, remarking to the next passer-by that the weather was a 'nice change.' It is a way we have in South Molton. When the water mains freeze, we ask each other if we are going to have a touch of winter.

January 1917 – The Destruction of Hallsands

The sorry saga of the demise of the Start Bay fishing village of Hallsands is not entirely weather-related. It is more a case of human folly. The tiny village was built on a ledge, above a shingly beach, beneath a dark-coloured cliff. A mile or so north of Start Point, it faced east, looking up the English Channel. When the prevailing westerlies blew, it was sheltered, but when it roared from the opposite direction it was in direct line of fire, like the seafronts at Seaton, Sidmouth and Torquay. At such times, the village's protection was its beach, this absorbing the fury, power and might of the waves. However, in 1897 permission was granted to dredge half a million tons of shingle from a short way offshore. Protests followed. Engineers maintained that the natural pattern of currents in Start Bay would fill up any holes left by the dredging.

Soon after work commenced, the beach at Hallsands began to disappear; within a few years it had dropped in level by 13 feet. Now exposed to the elements, the village suffered on those

occasions when winds of an easterly nature occurred with any strength. Through the first decade of the 20th century there were some years of peace and some of destruction; the damage was generally made good. But in late January 1917 the village was essentially destroyed. It is fortunate that nobody was killed, as there were some narrow escapes.

Today, many people make a pilgrimage to see the village. As the original road down the cliff to the village is impassable, a viewing platform has been created. A full account is given in another of my books – *The Story of Hallsands*.

18 July 1926 – "What the Hell was That?"

A violent storm resulted in a 'fire-ball' travelling down the chimney of a cottage near Okehampton. It blew out the entire grate, removed a door from its hinges, and split a granite post, in the garden, clean in two. Although taken completely by surprise, nobody was hurt.

27 February 1928 – Iced Diamonds

Now you see it… the Revd H. Hugh Breton recorded that: *Dartmoor was swept by an ice-storm of an intensity of which there is no known precedent… The whole moor is covered in a sheet of ice… This is called Amel (old English word which means enamel) and is caused by super-cooled rain… which immediately freezes on the first object it touches… When the sun came out in the afternoon… the country presented an amazing scene – every hedge and tree laden with ice and every blade of grass an icicle – and lit upon by the sunshine, displayed all the colours of the rainbow. In the strong wind the iced sticks clinked against each other like little bells, and ice crackled like paper. When the sun went behind a cloud much of the beauty was gone.*

17 November 1928 – A Wind up the Willows

Just as it was 13 years earlier, this exposed market town was in the news again, but for a different type of weather: *SOUTH MOLTON – The gale was the worst here for many years, and resulted in considerable damage to property. Lamp-posts were blown down or damaged, trees uprooted, and garden stuff blown about in pieces. Roofs suffered badly, falling slates and weather boards rendering it dangerous to walk in the streets. Two windows in the hosiery establishment of Mr John Rockey were wrecked, fragments of glass being blown more than sixty feet away. Before the contents of the windows could be removed many garments were blown into the street and retrieved by passers-by. So great was the force of the wind, which was accompanied by heavy rain, that stationary motor cars were moved. When the gale was at its height, the noise made by the telephone wires was extraordinary.*

September 1929 – Bed Wetting with a Difference!

Whenever I visit Okehampton, I always like to have a joke about the wetness of the weather with Rita, an assistant manager in a large shop in the town. I usually find that I leave Exeter basking in the nicest day imaginable, but as I drive along the A30 towards the great bulk of Cawsand Hill, on the northern extreme of Dartmoor, rainclouds seem to bubble up; by the time the moorland town is reached, it's pouring! Of course, Rita always likes to champion the idea that Okehampton is no wetter than anywhere else… The following report supports *my* side of the story!

Owing to the heavy rain on Saturday several places were flooded. Towards night the conditions became very bad, and the rivers rose rapidly. The worst case was at the Poor-law Institution, where about 11 p.m. the West Ockment, which runs within a few feet of the Institution, overflowed and in a short time the ground floor of the building was covered with water to a depth of between three and four feet. The casual wards are on the ground floor, and ten men, three women, and a child had to be removed through the windows. Beds were floating about. The store was also flooded and provisions, etc, spoiled. The Clerk's office was inundated and books, files, letters and furniture were floating about. Panels of doors were knocked out to let the water escape. The piggeries and fowl houses were also flooded, 25 fowls being drowned. The pigs, however, were got to safety.

Messrs Blatchford, Ash and Co's saw mills were flooded from the East Ockment, which runs at the back of the timber works. The bridge which was recently erected at Fatherford was washed away, as was the one at the end of Simmons Park. Messrs Fulford had a quantity of manure spoiled by water, which entered the stores at the back of Market-street.

Owing to the bad weather conditions, play in the match between Okehampton and Bideford had to be abandoned ten minutes after the interval, there being no score.

June 1932 – A Monumental Storm

For those sailors who came home to Bideford in past times, there were, on either side of the Torridge, two elevated landmarks to tell them that their journey was nearly done. The press reported on the fate of one of them: *A granite obelisk, 50 feet high, standing in the grounds of Tapeley House, on high ground on the east bank of the River Torridge, near Instow, and which for more than seventy years has been a prominent landmark, visible at a considerable distance, was struck by lightning and demolished during a brief but severe thunderstorm which broke over the district on Saturday morning.*

The storm did not appear to cover a wide area, and at Barnstaple only a little of the thunder could be heard. When the lightning struck the obelisk some huge blocks of granite, with which it was constructed, were hurled a distance of a hundred feet, and in falling became embedded in the ground, whilst the iron railings surrounding the memorial were bent and twisted into fantastic shapes. Fragments of railings and masonry were scattered in all directions. The base of the monument is now all that remains intact, with the ancient cannon mounted at each corner.

The obelisk was erected in 1856 by public subscription in memory of Archibald Cleveland, cornet of the 17th Lancers, who with two other officers alone survived the epic charge at Balaclava, and who was killed by the bursting of a shell at Inkerman.

July 1936 – The Cruel Sea

This article, from the middle of July 1936, at the height of the summer season, is just one of many to show how brutal and destructive wave-power can be, whatever the season: *The weather, bad as it had already been during this summer, played one of the most scurvy tricks ever known on some of the South Devon coast towns, especially Dawlish, early this morning.*

The wind commenced to rise last night, and slowly but surely the sea was beaten by a touch of the south-easterly wind into a raging mass, which at high tide, shortly before 7 o' clock, brought devastation and complete destruction to large numbers of huts on the beach below King's Walk and in Coryton Cove.

On the main beach below *King's Walk* [named at the time to celebrate the Coronation of Edward VII] *nine or ten huts were lifted bodily from their anchorage, swept away by the angry beating of the waves, smashed literally to smithereens, and washed together in a mass of wreckage underneath the breakwater.*

It was one of the most amazing sights ever seen in Dawlish in July. In September, perhaps, yes, but July – never before. The 'old salts' who gathered at the boat cove were this morning looking out over the scene of desolation and they agreed to a man that they had never known July to be so treacherous. Some of the huts, filled with all the paraphernalia for beach enjoyment, were carried over a hundred yards and shattered to fragments against the sea wall.

During the morning crowds entered into the work of trying to salve what they could of the wreckage, although in the midst of such havoc and destruction it was well-nigh impossible to find anything that was whole or sound. The piles of smashed woodwork can only find an end as firewood.

Coryton Cove did not suffer with quite the same severity, but at least eight beach huts are damaged and many of their contents are irretrievably smashed or soaked with sea and rain.

Cushions, stoves, chairs and mirrors, and a hundred odds and ends, were strewn over the beach. At ten o' clock it looked as if every handcart available in the town had been borrowed to take away salvage.

To many of the visitors the sight has brought a thrill, but the faces of most of those who looked down on the picture of their huts in fragments were full of dismay. For quite a number this is the second disaster that they have faced within twelve months. Last September similar havoc was wrought, but then it was at the end of the season and they were able to laugh off their misfortunes, but this morning's trail of devastation at the height of the supposed summer season is another tale.

Here and there a saving touch of humour was seen. One lady, her hair swept in tangles by the wind and matted with rain, could not forbear a smile and joke about the "happy home" as she was met by friends endeavouring to get away from the beach with a battered kettle, a jug, a couple of deckchairs and a shapeless cushion or two...

Lessees of beach refreshment kiosks and bathing tents are despondent. They have had a bad season... "The visitors are here, and if we do get a fine day they flock to the beach, but the next there is little or nothing doing owing to the weather. Nothing seems settled."

4 May 1937 – "Not Much We Can Do Here, Boys!"

This next story illustrates the local nature of weather: *Heavy thunderstorms broke in many parts of Devon this afternoon and did some considerable damage in some areas. Two cottages at Lockgate, near Bow, were struck by what is believed to have been a thunderbolt, and were destroyed by fire. Debris was thrown some distance by the explosion. The cottages were unoccupied.*

Most of East Devon escaped the storm till much later in the afternoon. Newton Abbot also reported sunshine, but Bovey Tracey had very heavy thunder soon after lunch. There seemed to be little lightning, and the rain was not heavy.

Lockgate is about four miles from Bow, off the main road, and Crediton Fire Brigade raced along twelve miles of winding lanes in a heavy thunderstorm and lashing rain to the fire. Smoke was discovered issuing from the roof by Mr F. Webber, who phoned for the brigade from 'Spestos.' On arrival they found that lightning had struck the chimney and ignited the thatch. The cottages, which had been unoccupied since Lady Day, were doomed, and, as the nearest water supply was 4¹/₂ miles away, and no other property was in danger, the captain of the Brigade, Mr G. Burrows, decided it was not necessary to get to work. In the centre of the road was found a piece of the brick from the chimney, which had been dislodged by the lightning.

At Exeter the storm was in every sense a 'well-behaved' storm. It gave ample warning of its approach by way of a slowly darkening sky, and the rain began very gradually. The thunder and lightning were not severe, and the rain was most welcome to owners of gardens and to farmers being insufficiently heavy to do much, if any, damage.

Additionally, the storm served to clear the rather sultry atmosphere of the morning, and is not likely seriously to interfere with the run of fine weather.

It was the first rain for some weeks in Exeter, and corresponded with the first day of the Coronation decorations, which did not appear to have been damaged.

1940 – Cold Comfort

The unusual and rare phenomenon of freezing rain occurred on several consecutive days. The naked branches of many trees were coated in several layers of ice; as they became progressively heavier, they could not be supported and broke off. The Exe estuary at Starcross froze for the first time since 1891, as did the Taw above and below the Long Bridge at Barnstaple. One lady living at Ilsington, on eastern Dartmoor, took a bath. For some reason she didn't get out; her body was later found encased in a solid block of ice!

1947 – Sub-tropical Salcombe?

Much is made of the mildness of the climate of sunny, sheltered Salcombe, and it's certainly true that the garden at Overbecks, on the south side of this small sailing resort, bears a distinctly sub-tropical and exotic appearance. However, this next extract, from B. F. Harvey, appeared in an early 1950s guide book to Kingsbridge. It was about a spell of cruel weather in 1947, which some people may recall with a degree of clarity, at a normally mild and benign Soar Mill Cove, the only deep depression in a run of high cliffs between Bolt Head and Bolt Tail: *It was a different story in the early weeks of 1947. Then the lovely, friendly valley was frozen and cruel. Snow lay in impassable drifts across the hills, and the shore was bound in ice. Hundreds and thousands of birds driven further and further south and west came at last to the end of the land, and starved and frozen had no strength to put out to sea to find a warmer country.*

But the most striking thing of all was the absence of some of the small birds whose bodies were never found. Previously a pair of Stonechats had lived at the junction of the two streams; at any time of the year they could be seen there… Now the spot was silent. There was no rattle as of little pebbles to greet you as you passed. For twelve months never a Stonechat appeared; until this spring when once more a nest was built and at this moment a pair are feeding three almost fully-fledged youngsters again along the edge of the tiny brook.

It was as well that places like Salcombe and Hope Cove were near the sea, as this was the only way provisions could be brought in.

3 March 1951 – "Lighten our Darkness"

Exeter City's first soccer match under floodlights was scheduled to be played against Plymouth Argyle, but dense fog caused a postponement.

Six days later, it was a case of second time lucky for Exeter City as the fog stayed away and their first night match, under the glare of some brilliant floodlights, went ahead against their old foe, Plymouth Argyle. Alas, the Argyle players adjusted more quickly to the illuminated pitch and ran out 3-0 winners.

August 1952 – The Lynmouth Flood Disaster

The streams in the vicinity of Lynmouth, 'where Exmoor meets the sea', all have a steep profile. From the towering heights of the moor down to the sea is a long drop in a short distance. Whenever it rains on the high ground of Exmoor for any length of time, the streams have a tendency to rise very quickly.

The summer of 1952 had been particularly wet, and much rain had been absorbed by the high ground in the watershed above Lynmouth. Therefore it was a cruel hand of nature that then turned the screw by launching the most incredible and prolonged downpour witnessed in these parts in over two centuries.

Prior to the night of 15 August 1952, more than nine inches of rain had fallen in less than 24 hours. These statistics may be meaningless to those who are not familiar with meteorological data. It is probably easier to understand the concept that three months of average rainfall fell in less than a single day – an estimated 90 million gallons! The moors, already saturated, could absorb no more rainfall; as the clouds burst vast amounts of water poured straight off the land into the various stream systems. Lynmouth, at the bottom of the hill, was ultimately submerged by the combined efforts of all these rivers heading towards it with a fury that was unabated and merciless. The lower parts of the village, crowded in a peak week of holiday time, stood little chance.

Normally Lynmouth had about 450 residents, but the time of year meant that the figure had, more or less, trebled. It was the worst-case scenario, to quote a more modern cliché. If you double the speed, width and depth of a stream, then you increase its capability to erode by some 64 times. Here the situation was more extreme even than that; the heavens contrived to create such raging torrents that they swept almost all before them. Sheep innocently grazing on the high moors were found drowned five miles out in the Bristol Channel. Boulders weighing up to ten tons were carried along with the current. But what of poor Lynmouth?

Conditions couldn't have been much worse for the townsfolk, or the many visitors unlucky enough to be there that night when chaos and catastrophe after catastrophe occurred in the darkness. Immense damage was caused as the rising flood engulfed waterfront properties, removing walls and buildings almost as if they had been built out of balsa rather than brick.

The Rhenish Tower, which stood on the harbour breakwater, was destroyed in the flood, but was later replaced by a replica, shown in this picture. The original tower was the idea of Colonel Rawden. In the early 19th century he cunningly created it to house a salt water supply to feed his home, so that he never went short of bath water.

Despite its closeness to the mouth of the river, the famous Rising Sun pub survived, as the waters rose only to a point just in front of its doorway. There were many staying there at the time, and this number was boosted by people taking refuge after having attended a local concert. They may well have raised a toast to a projecting spur known as Turbal Rock, because this penned back the flood waters.

Naturally, on this terrible night it was the human loss of life that was the real cause of so much grief. The death toll rose to 34 (nine of them children), of whom one poor lady was never identified; ten were holidaymakers, two of them young ladies from Australia; and the rest were all local people.

The task of sorting out the aftermath was colossal, as one might imagine. There were heroes that night and afterwards. The plight of the tiny resort touched the hearts of many and the village was showered by kindness from almost every part of the world. Although the media coverage was limited at that time, everyone seemed to know of this disaster; people still talk of it and write about it, so it won't be forgotten. Hopefully the costly engineering measures taken to alleviate any similar deluges will spare the community a repeat of this devastating disaster.

September 1954 – A Carnival Atmosphere

Just when you thought it was safe to proceed… *Chudleigh Carnival – (Saturday) And now we come to the final day, which opened dull, but cleared up, and the judging was carried out in Beechwood Meadow in bright sunshine. Some forty minutes later, when the head of the procession got as far as Colway Lane, there came a violent thunderstorm, with tremendous hail, and thunder and lightning, and those taking part with the bands were drenched to the skin. It was the heaviest rain we have seen in Chudleigh in many a year.*

September – October 1960 – Wet! Wet! Wet!

It never rains…Those who anticipated an Indian summer, after an extremely wet one, didn't bargain for an Indian monsoon season! A brief diary of events reveals the following:

28 September: Rain started falling heavily; although Teignmouth and Exmouth experienced an inch of rainfall in a very short time, it was Plymouth that had the initial floods.

29 September: It continued to rain; the railway line was submerged at Plympton.

30 September: Exeter and East Devon bore the brunt of a deluge, almost three inches following in 24 hours. This would be almost 'a month's worth'. The lower parts of Crediton suffered when the Yeo burst its banks at Fordton, near the town's railway station. Several older properties collapsed. At Exton a small thatched church suffered the same fate. Exeter became almost an island, surrounded on several sides by rivers and streams that had burst their banks. Teignmouth, Kingsteignton and the Torridge valley were all problem areas.

1 October: And just when they thought that things couldn't worsen… three inches of rain fell in about an hour and a half! The Axe and Coly valleys, which merge near Colyford, became a huge

expanse of flood water. An Australian visitor was rescued by boat, but died from a heart attack. There were more floods in the Exeter and Crediton areas; throughout South Devon emergency crews were thwarted in their gallant efforts to save man and beast by landslides and mudslides blocking railways and roads.

2 October: There was a brief respite early in the day and mopping-up activities began in earnest, but by tea-time it was pouring with rain again; with the ground saturated, the roads and railways were again badly affected.

3 October: Some real relief was now afforded as clearing up began again and hopes were high as the following few days yielded little rainfall; the river systems began to flush vast amounts of brown water through to the sea.

6 October: But the dry spell was short lived, proving to be just another false dawn as, in the evening, the heavens opened. The nether parts of Exmouth were swamped, particularly the area of dense terraced housing referred to as 'The Colony'. Crediton was again devastated: the town was completely cut off by road and rail for several hours. There was flooding all over North Devon, the Lyn being watched in horror by those who had seen it wreak death and destruction less than a decade earlier.

8 October: Strong winds and high tides proved to be a wicked combination, as floods were experienced in many places. Torquay, Tiverton and Exmoor were some of the places to suffer. Sir Michael Joseph, then Minister of Housing and Local Government, visited Exmouth to inspect the damage to property. Then there was something of an interlude. The days got shorter, the autumn arrived, and so did the rains…

Cowick St, Exeter

22 October: Two boys were drowned and a third person died from a heart attack as a direct consequence of his flooded situation. More than a hundred houses were flooded at Sidmouth. Ottery St Mary, no stranger to flooding, had waters pouring along its main street. The lower parts of Exeter were inundated once more.

23 October: More flooding in East Devon; Bridport, over the border into Dorset, had water which was five feet deep in places.

26 October: Two inches of rain fell on Exeter, bringing the total so far for the month to a staggering 15.2 inches, almost half the average annual amount. All the rivers of the county began to rise rapidly…

27 October: And they continued to rise to the highest levels witnessed in the 20th century! Every valley saw flooding; the worst hit were those of the Exe, Culm, Taw and Torridge. In Exeter the situation was so grave that the BBC (no local radio in those days!) interrupted programmes to broadcast messages to the thousands of people marooned in shops and offices in the lower parts of the city. Almost a thousand properties in the St Thomas and Marsh Barton areas were flooded at ground level, and those inside sought refuge either on the first floor, or, in the absence of one, on the roof! Exeter was fortunate then to have a strong military presence in the city, and a convoy of amphibious vehicles set to work. There was also a number of people who had their own small rowing boats or canoes. They could never have imagined that they would ever use them on the city streets! Nevertheless, there were many commuters who were stranded and could not get home that night. Those at risk were somehow

Okehampton St, Exeter

helped to higher ground, there being some brave and bold rescues effected in the surging waters.

28 October: Many prayers were answered; the rain stopped falling, the river levels swiftly subsided and the huge task of cleaning up the aftermath began. It was a soul-destroying time for many whose homes had been wrecked.

When people began to realise that the worst was over, there were a few lighter moments, such as when a girl in a bikini turned the eyes of passing men as she walked along the flooded streets of Exeter. Unfortunately a flag day had to be aborted, despite its being in aid of the Shipwrecked Mariners' Society!

28 December 1962 – Running Out of Steam

The snow came too late for Christmas Day, but within days blizzard conditions rendered most of Dartmoor's roads impassable. The weather remained constantly cold and snowy right through to the following 7 March; through this wintry period supplies to remote places like Postbridge and Bellever were intermittent. The Royal Marines, so adept in such conditions, used a four-wheel drive Landrover to tow a sledge to Postbridge with provisions.

Devon's Wild & Wicked Weather

In the north of the county, Lynton and Lynmouth, served by alpine roads, were also effectively cut off from the outside world. As the days passed the food shortage became so acute that a mercy mission saw helicopters fly in with more than a thousand loaves of bread.

The next day, in blizzard conditions, the last passenger train, mourned in a mock funeral, set out at 6.20 p.m. to travel between Tavistock South and Plymouth.

The train which set out at 6.20 p.m. from Tavistock South arrived in Plymouth at 12.25 a.m.

Princetown

January 1963 – A Winter of Discontent

This was followed by a respite of snowless days, but another great fall followed on 3 January 1963, continuing the long spell of extreme winter weather. Snow fell on 27 days. It was officially the coldest winter in England (and Wales) since 1740. Day after day, anticyclones to the north and east of the British Isles brought bitterly cold winds from the east. The earlier blizzard over South-west England and South Wales on 29 and 30 December had 'warmed things up' ready for what was about to follow. Life had been brought to a virtual standstill, with all the inevitable consequences.

It made life particularly difficult for Mr Tom Dobbin. He had relocated to Torquay with the intention of building

Princetown

a model village (now the famous Babbacombe Model Village). In starting from scratch, he hoped to plant it out ready for business the following summer. Working in extreme conditions, he found it so difficult to acquire and nurture enough bedding plants that he was obliged to buy his own nursery.

Babbacombe

Meanwhile, as Tom was slaving away on the groundwork for the village, children across the county availed themselves of the opportunities afforded by closed schools. Snow-covered hillsides and frozen ponds made the perfect playground for fun and games. This picture shows the River Exe near the Port Royal pub in Exeter.

The Sun-baked Summer of 1976 – High and Dry

If you had wanted to guarantee a summer in which to hold a barbecue, this was it. But with next to no precipitation falling from April onwards, there was a price to pay. Standpipes! It was as if somebody had pulled the plug on Dartmoor's reservoirs, as levels started to drop. At Fernworthy Reservoir, about three miles from Chagford, bridges, which hadn't been seen for quite some years, were exposed. Someone had some fun with the press; they posed a skeleton on a fold-up stool, complete with fishing rod and protected by a sunshade.

In terms of tourism, it was a superb summer: ice-cream and beer and, later on, bucket sales went through the roof. However, on a day-to-day level, things became increasingly hot and there were grave concerns about water supply. Cows exacerbated the situation: with a shortage of lush grass, they compensated by drinking even more water!

In desperation the Government appointed Dennis Howell as Minister for Drought, to co-ordinate water conservation. Within three days it started raining. Opposition members were quick to point out that this should have been done earlier, suggesting that Mr Howell was some sort of 'rainmaker'.

Measures had been employed to ration the meagre water resources; standpipes became a common sight in parts of the county. In a bizarre twist of fate, they were still in use when the heavens opened in September; newspapers carried pictures of people queuing for water whilst dressed in all manner of rainwear.

Unfortunately, when the rains came, they outstayed their welcome; the driest summer on record was followed by the wettest autumn!

25 January 1990 – Give Us a Wave!

A record wind speed of 97 miles per hour was measured at Plymouth, and immense waves battered the coastline.

A stormy scene at Meadfoot Bay, Torquay

The storm caused a trail of death (four fatalities in the South-West) and immense destruction. The former Torbay Aircraft Museum, at Barton Pines, suffered considerable damage; the spire of Hatherleigh's parish church of St John the Baptist was blown over; as was a large lorry when trying to negotiate an exposed Tamar Bridge.

December 2000 – A Dawlish Warren Downpour

The Coastguard co-ordinated an overnight rescue at the Hazelwood Park caravan park at Dawlish Warren, on 7–8 December, which saw 160 mainly elderly residents, cats, dogs and a parrot rowed in an Environment Agency inflatable boat, or airlifted by the Chivenor-based air-sea rescue helicopter, to dry ground. They were then taken to Dawlish Leisure Centre.

Running through the park, the Shutterton Brook, normally an anonymous watercourse, was just one small stream of a great many in Devon to overflow its banks. The situation arose at the end of one of the wettest autumns, when the ground simply could absorb no more water. Coinciding with a high tide, the waters of the stream, unable to disperse into the Exe estuary, were ponded back.

On the same night two people from East Village were drowned at Cheriton Fitzpaine when their car was washed away by another, equally small brook which was in spate.

Meanwhile, the landlord and landlady of the Cowley Bridge Inn, on the northern outskirts of Exeter, called time on their pub for the last time. Situated perilously close to the Exe, Gordon and Maureen Henderson had had enough. They had been forced to close in October through flooding, and, after refurbishment, had just reopened when they were inundated again. The timing was cruel, as their insurance for such a situation had expired just days before the second flood, and the insurers had declined to renew the policy. However, to their credit, the Heavitree Brewery, which owns the pub, agreed to stump up the money to put it back to rights.

25 January 2001 – A Lucky Escape

On this day, Ivybridge's library was struck by lightning! Fortunately it was closed at the time of the strike. At work in a corner, the sole librarian on duty must have been shocked to see a bright flash pass through a window and home in on the telephone system, which exploded with a loud bang. Had the library been open, then the person delegated with the task of collecting returned books would have stood right in its path...

August 2004 – Watered Down Beer

I had just published a little book about Beer, and had mentioned previous floods in the village, but was taken aback to see the worst flood 'in living memory' rip through it, causing an immense amount of damage. In particular, the hillside graveyard was devastated by a landslip. However, a few weeks later, on 16 August, all this paled by comparison as Boscastle, on the north Cornish coast, suffered a much worse flash flood, reminiscent of that of Lynmouth more than a half a century earlier. Unlike its North Devon counterpart, however, there was no loss of life.

In Conclusion – Some Homespun Weather Wisdom

And so it goes on. But is there anything we can learn from all this? The examples given seem to suggest that certain rules of thumb should prevail.

Don't buy (or build) a house on a flood plain (or sand dunes) or at the bottom of a steep hill with underlying clay. The picture below is of Dawlish Warren at the mouth of the Exe estuary. The first house was erected on the outer Warren in 1899; storms accounted for many houses over the following decades and the very last one – 'White Shanty' – disappeared in 1960.

Consider the potential threat of living in coastal villages, however beautiful, where steep rivers run sharply down to the sea. Beer, Boscastle, Polperro and Lynmouth are all examples of this.

We all know that you shouldn't stand under trees during thunderstorms; as we have seen, churches are not necessarily the sanctuaries we might hope for, either.

Don't venture close to storm waves as they break over the coast. And if your dog jumps, or is washed, into the sea, don't throw yourself in to save him or her: the chances are the dog will survive – but you won't!

When spring tides and strong onshore winds are about to combine, check the tide times before you walk along any beach, or around any headlands.

Don't create work for the various rescue groups by walking on high ground, such as Dartmoor or Exmoor, when the weather pundits predict strong winds and substantial amounts of drifting snowfall.

But if you do go walking in such areas, dress in appropriate fashion.

In snowy weather, keep a wary eye out for the Devil.

In hot, dry summers, dampen your thatch roof from time to time.

There's a pub at Dawlish Warren whimsically called the Sunburnt Arms. To my knowledge there isn't yet one called 'Snowed Inn'. If there was, it would surely have to be on the Moors! So, if you don't want to be cut off from civilisation in the depths of winter, don't live in Princetown.

But, when all is said and done, the stories in this book are not really a true reflection of weather in Devon; only the extremes tend to make the news! In fact, many of the extremes noted here are fairly commonplace in other parts of the country: we often walk around in our shirtsleeves watching the snow ploughs on television clearing blocked roads in the north of England or over the Scottish Highlands. There is good reason why so many people come to Devon for their holidays and many also to retire – with its infinite variety and changeability, our weather is what helps to make our landscape so lovely.

Glorious Devon, indeed!